Through Lent with Jesus

An activity book for children

Katie Thompson

Kevin
Mayhew

First published in 2000 by
KEVIN MAYHEW LTD
Buxhall
Stowmarket
Suffolk IP14 3BW

0 1 2 3 4 5 6 7 8 9

ISBN 1 84003 655 9
Cat No 1500396

Cover design by Jonathan Stroulger
Edited by Katherine Laidler and Peter Dainty
Typesetting by Louise Selfe
Printed and bound in Great Britain

Introduction

Every year, as the days begin to lengthen, we observe the season of Lent in preparation for the great feast of Easter. Lent isn't just about giving up chocolate or sweets. It needn't be unpleasant or boring either. It should be a positive time when we do something special for God, allowing us to draw closer to him and become more familiar with his Gospel of love.

This little book will allow you to do just that in a thoroughly enjoyable way! Starting with Ash Wednesday, there is a short passage to read and a puzzle to do each day, as the events leading up to the joy of Easter Sunday unfold.

Use the clues to find out what the word Lent means

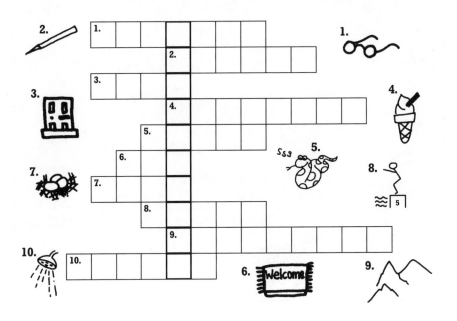

Ash Wednesday

The temptations (1)

Jesus was led by the Holy Spirit into the desert where the devil came to tempt him. After fasting for forty days and nights Jesus was very hungry, and the devil said to him, 'If you are indeed the Son of God, turn the stones around you into bread.'

In reply, Jesus repeated words of Scripture . . .

Matthew 4:1-4

Match the words with the answer Jesus gave!

Day 2

The temptations (2)

Then the devil took Jesus to the Temple in Jerusalem and together they stood on its highest point. 'If you are the Son of God,' the devil said, 'then throw yourself down to prove it, because Scripture tells us that God's angels will protect you from harm.'

Again Jesus answered him with words from Scripture . . .

Matthew 4:5-7

Day 3

The temptations (3)

The devil did not give up easily, so he took Jesus to the top of a high mountain where he showed him the kingdoms of the world in all their glory. 'If you worship me,' the devil said, 'I will give all of these to you.'

Finally growing impatient, Jesus said . . .

Matthew 4:8-11

TEST 3

I will give you the world if you worship me

Z 1	M 14
Y 2	L 15
X 3	K 16
W 4	J 17
V 5	I 18
U 6	H 19
T 7	G 20
S 8	F 21
R 9	E 22
Q 10	D 23
P 11	C 24
O 12	B 25
N 13	A 26

```
25 22    20 12 13 22
_____!
8  26 7  26 13

2 12 6    14 6 8 7

4 12 9 8 19 18 11

20 12 23    26 15 12 13 22
```

Day 4

Jesus begins to preach

Soon after John the Baptist's arrest, Jesus travelled throughout Galilee proclaiming the Gospel and saying to the people, 'The kingdom of God is very near! Turn away from sin and believe the Good News.'

Mark 1:14-15

'Repent and believe the Good News!'

D	N	A	B	U	R	R
S	D	L	G	S	P	E
E	E	O	Q	W	V	P
O	O	M	S	E	R	E
D	G	J	I	N	K	N
A	F	L	P	Q	R	T
C	E	S	J	D	H	B
B	A	S	P	E	K	E

REPENT

AND

BELIEVE

THE

GOOD

NEWS

First Sunday

The first disciples

One day, as he was walking by the Sea of Galilee, Jesus saw two brothers out fishing together. Their names were Simon Peter and Andrew. Jesus spoke to them and said, 'Come, follow me, and I will make you fishers of people.'

The two brothers left their boat and nets at once, and followed him.

A little further on Jesus saw James and John, mending nets with their father, Zebedee. Again, Jesus asked them to follow him, and they left their father and went with him.

Matthew 4:18-22

What did Jesus say which made these fishermen follow him?

Use the secret code pad to read his words!

SECRET CODE PAD

A (1) B (2) C (3) D (4) E (5) F (6) G (7) H (8) I (9) J (10)
K (11) L (12) M (13) N (14) O (15) P (16) Q (17) R (18)
S (19) T (20) U (21) V (22) W (23) X (24) Y (25) Z (26)

'

__ __ __ __ __ __ __ __ __ __ __ __
(3) (15) (13) (5)   (6) (15) (12) (12) (15) (23)   (13) (5)

__ __ __ __ __ __ __ __
(1) (14) (4)   (9)   (23) (9) (12) (12)

__ __ __ __ __ __ __
(13) (1) (11) (5)   (25) (15) (21)

__ __ __ __ __ __ __ __ __
(6) (9) (19) (8) (5) (18) (19)   (15) (6)

__ __ __ __ __ __ ,
(16) (5) (15) (16) (12) (5)

Day 6

The first miracle

Jesus and his mother, together with his disciples, were invited to a wedding in a town called Cana. There was food to eat and wine to drink, and the celebrations carried on throughout the evening.

Then Mary came to Jesus and said, 'Son, there is no more wine for the guests to drink.'

'Why do you ask for help when my time has not yet come?' Jesus asked.

But Mary turned to the servants and said to them, 'Do whatever Jesus tells you.'

Nearby stood six very large water jars, and Jesus told the servants to fill them with water. 'Now pour some out and take it to the head waiter,' he said.

The water had been changed to wine, and when he had tasted it the head waiter went to the bridegroom and said, 'Sir, you have certainly saved the very best wine until last!'

This was the first miracle Jesus performed and it happened at Cana in Galilee. His disciples had witnessed his glory and they believed in him.

John 2:1-11

Can you spot eight differences in the bottom picture?

Day 7

Healing and teaching

Jesus travelled throughout Galilee proclaiming the Good News and teaching the crowds who gathered to listen to him. Everywhere he went, he cured the sick and healed every kind of disease. News of the marvellous miracles he had performed quickly spread, and people suffering from all kinds of illnesses travelled from far and wide to be cured by him.

Matthew 4:23-25

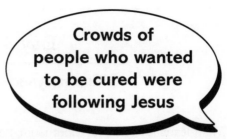

Crowds of people who wanted to be cured were following Jesus

Can you find ten differences in the bottom picture?

Day 8

The paralysed man (1)

Cap~er~num

When Jesus returned to Capernaum, news soon spread that he was there, and crowds of people gathered outside the house where he was staying.

As Jesus was preaching, four men carrying a stretcher arrived. The man on the stretcher was paralysed and could not walk, and his friends hoped that Jesus would cure him. Because the crowds were so large they could not carry the stretcher close to Jesus. So they climbed on to the roof and made a hole above where Jesus was standing. Then they lowered the stretcher down gently on long ropes.

Seeing their faith, Jesus turned to the man on the stretcher and said to him, 'My son, your sins are forgiven.'

Mark 2:1-5

If we have faith in God, he will forgive us from our sins. Let us show God that we love him and trust in him

Day 9

The paralysed man (2)

Some of the scribes who were there were shocked and angry when they heard what Jesus had said. 'Who does he think he is!' they exclaimed. 'Only God has the power to forgive sins.'

Knowing what they were thinking, Jesus asked, 'Is it easier to forgive this man's sins, or to make him walk? If you need proof that I have the power to forgive sins, then I shall say to this man, "Stand up! Pick up your stretcher and walk!"'

The man then got to his feet and began to walk.

The people were amazed by this, and began praising God. 'Never have we seen anything like it!' they said.

Mark 2:6-12

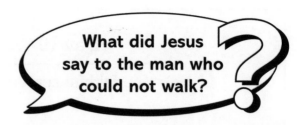

Write the next letter of the alphabet on the line above. For example, E will be written above D

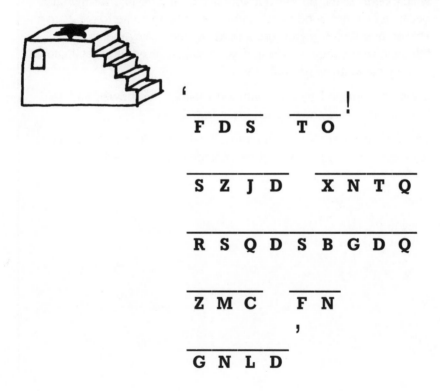

‘ ___ ___ !
F D S   T O

___
S Z J D   X N T Q

___
R S Q D S B G D Q

___
Z M C   F N
,

___
G N L D

A B C D E F G H I J K L M N O P Q R S T U V W X Y Z

Day 10

The faithful centurion

While Jesus was in Capernaum, some of the Jews came to him to ask for help. They had been sent by a Roman centurion whose favourite servant was very ill and close to death. 'Jesus, please help this man, because he has always been fair and kind to us,' they said.

Jesus went with them, but on the way they were met by some of the centurion's friends with a message for Jesus from the centurion which said, 'Jesus, do not put yourself to any trouble for my sake, because I am not good enough to expect you to come to me. I am a soldier, and I obey my orders just as my men obey me. Whatever I tell them to do, they will do it. If you will just give the order, I know that my servant will be well again.'

Jesus was amazed by the centurion's faith in his power, and said, 'Few people have shown such great trust in me.'

When the centurion's friends returned to his house they found great rejoicing because the servant had completely recovered.

Luke 7:1-10

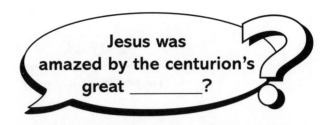

Jesus was amazed by the centurion's great _____?

**Write the word that fits the clue.
The first letter of the words will spell out the answer**

CLUES

1. Birds can do this

2. Place where planes land and take off

3. Liquid that flows from pens

4. A slow-moving reptile with a shell on its back

5. The opposite of sad

| 1 | 2 | 3 | 4 | 5 | ! |

Day 11

Treasure and pearl

Jesus compared the kingdom of heaven to priceless treasure as he said:

> One day a man was digging in a field when his spade struck a box which was buried there. When he opened the box he was amazed to find it was full of treasure. He quickly buried the treasure again, went away and sold his house and all that he owned. With the money he made, he bought the field from the farmer, and then ran back and dug up the treasure.

> *Matthew 13:44*

Then Jesus compared the kingdom of heaven to a precious pearl worth selling everything to own!

How many pearls can you count in this jumbled picture?

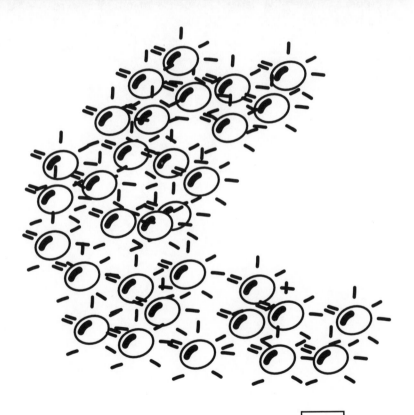

Answer

Second Sunday

Seeds

Jesus said to his disciples:

The kingdom of heaven is like a man who scatters seed in his field. Hour by hour, through daylight and darkness, the seeds send out shoots and roots, and begin to grow. The man does not know how this all happens, but before long his field is full of crops, and when the harvest is ripe the man begins to reap what he has sown.

Mark 4:26-29

Jesus told another parable about the tiny mustard seed

Can you fit these words into the boxes to complete this poem?

ME

WIDE

SEE

SMALL

TALL

HIDE

A mustard seed is very ⬚⬚⬚⬚⬚

and yet it grows so very T⬚⬚⬚

It puts out branches strong and W⬚⬚⬚

in which so many birds can ⬚⬚⬚⬚

God plants his words of love in ⬚⬚

and so his kingdom grows, you ⬚⬚⬚

Day 13

The Sower

Jesus began to teach the crowd, using parables to help them to understand his message:

One day a farmer went out to sow some seeds in his field. As he scattered the seeds some fell on the stony path at the edge of the field, where flocks of hungry birds flew down and gobbled them up. Some seeds fell on rocky ground where, although they sprouted, the soil was too shallow for their roots, and the baking hot sun shrivelled them up. Other seeds fell where weeds were growing, and the weeds choked them until they died. Some of the seeds landed on the farmer's richest soil, and grew into strong and healthy plants.

Matthew 13:3-9

Find the words missing from this poem

A _____ went, his _____ to sow,

he did not _____ if they would grow.

Some seeds fell on _____ ground,

some the hungry _____ soon found.

Some fell among the _____ so tall,

they stood no chance to _____ at all!

But some seeds fell on fertile _____ and

soon the _____ grew all around!

GROUND

THORNS

SEED

STONY

FARMER

KNOW

CROPS

BIRDS

GROW

Day 14

The twelve apostles

Jesus sent for the disciples he had chosen. When they arrived on the mountain where they had arranged to meet, he selected twelve from among them to be his apostles. They were chosen to share the Good News of God's kingdom with the world, and he gave them the power to heal people in his name. The names of the twelve were: Simon (whom Jesus called Peter), James, John, Andrew, Philip, Bartholomew, Matthew, Thomas, another apostle also called James, Thaddaeus, Simon and Judas.

Mark 3:13-18

TPREE   **WRENAD**   **ASJME**   **HONJ**

_____   _____   _____   _____

LIHPPI   **OOLWEMRTABH**   **SATHOM**   **HATTWEM**

_____   _____   _____   _____

SAMJE   **DDAETHAUS**   **MISON**   **DUJAS**

_____   _____   _____   _____

Day 15

Jesus is rejected

Jesus returned to his home town of Nazareth with his disciples, and on the Sabbath day he went to the synagogue to preach.

The people there were amazed by his wisdom and all that he said, and many of them had heard of the miracles that he had worked. But some of the crowd asked, 'Surely this is Joseph the carpenter's son? Isn't his family still living here in Nazareth? How can he know all these things and talk in this way?'

They would not listen to Jesus or believe in him.

Mark 6:1-5

The people would not accept him in his own town

Write the first letter of each picture on the line above to find out Jesus' reaction

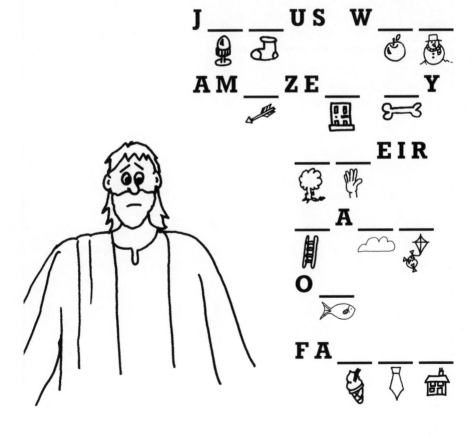

Day 16

Jesus calms the storm

Jesus and his disciples set off to sail to the other side of the Sea of Galilee. Jesus had been preaching all day, and he was soon lulled to sleep by the rocking of the boat. Suddenly a storm blew up, and great waves began to pound the boat. The disciples were terrified and ran to wake Jesus before they all drowned.

Jesus got up and, scolding the sea and wind, he said, 'Be at peace!'

At once the wind dropped and the sea grew calm again. Then Jesus asked his disciples, 'Why were you so afraid? Did you not believe in me?'

They were filled with wonder because they had seen that even the sea and wind would obey his commands.

Mark 4:35-41

Jesus and his disciples set off to cross to the other side of the lake

Which boat should they take?

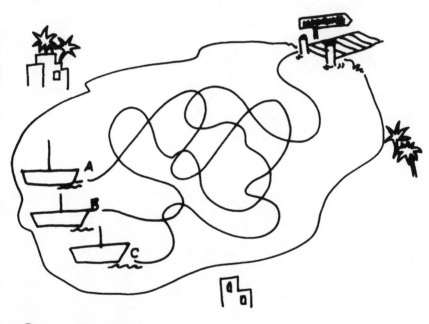

Day 17

Jesus feeds five thousand (1)

Jesus crossed the Sea of Galilee, and, seeing that a large crowd had followed him along the shore, he turned to Philip and asked, 'Where can we buy some bread to feed these people?'

Philip answered, 'Master, it would cost a fortune to give each person even a small piece of bread!'

Then Andrew brought to Jesus a young boy who had five loaves and two fish.

John 6:1-9

Jesus fed 5,000 people with five loaves and two fish! What do we call such an extraordinary event?

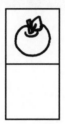

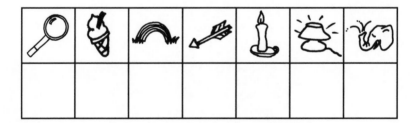

Day 18

Jesus feeds five thousand (2)

'What use are five loaves and two fish among all these people?' Andrew asked Jesus.

'Tell the people to sit down on the grass,' Jesus said, and, taking the bread and fish, he gave thanks to God, then gave the food out to as many as five thousand people, and there was plenty for everyone. When they had finished, they filled twelve baskets with the scraps that were left over from the five loaves and two fish.

John 6:9-12

Jesus told them to pick up the scraps so that nothing was wasted. How many baskets did they fill?

Solve the problems and use the code to spell out the answer

18	4	16	15	7	3
– 4	x 4	– 7	÷ 3	+5	x 3
___	___	___	___	___	___

___ ___ ___ ___ ___ ___

12	5	9	16	14
V	L	E	W	T

Third Sunday

Blind Bartimaeus

Jesus and his disciples were leaving Jericho with a crowd of followers, and a blind beggar called Bartimaeus was sitting at the roadside. When he heard that Jesus of Nazareth was passing, Bartimaeus began to shout loudly, 'Jesus, Son of David, have pity and help me!'

The crowd told him to calm down and be quiet, but Bartimaeus kept on shouting until Jesus heard his cries.

'Bring that man to me,' said Jesus, and they led Bartimaeus to him. 'What do you want me to do for you?' he asked.

Bartimaeus said, 'Master, give me sight so that I can see!'

Then Jesus told him, 'Go. Because you believe in me your sight has returned.'

Suddenly Bartimaeus could see clearly, and he set off at once to follow Jesus.

Mark 10:46-52

Like Bartimaeus, what do we need to have?

M = 8   A = 12   H = 7   J = 15   S = 21
P = 14   R = 9   F = 4   I = 3   T = 16

17	4	11	9	(3 x 3)
−13	x 3	− 8	+ 7	−2
___	___	___	___	___
___	___	___	___	___
___	___	___	___	___

I CAN SEE!

Day 20

The children's friend

People would often bring their children to Jesus to be blessed by him, and on one particular day the disciples sent the children away. But Jesus scolded his disciples and said, 'Let them come to me and do not stand in their way, for God's kingdom belongs to such as these. Anyone wishing to enter the kingdom of God must first become like one of these little children.'

Then he took the children in his arms and blessed each one of them.

Mark 10:13-16

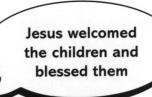

Jesus welcomed
the children and
blessed them

**Write the first letter of each object
to find the words of Jesus**

'

Mark 10:14

Day 21

Zacchaeus

Jesus went to a town called Jericho, where a man called Zacchaeus lived. Nobody liked Zacchaeus because he was a tax collector who cheated people to make himself rich.

When Jesus arrived, crowds gathered to see him and Zacchaeus was among them. Zacchaeus was very small and could not see Jesus because of the crowds, so he climbed a tree to get a better view. As Jesus passed by, he looked up and said, 'Come down, Zacchaeus! I want to visit your house today.'

Zacchaeus almost fell out of the tree with surprise. Hearing what Jesus had said, the crowd began to grumble and complain. 'How can Jesus speak to such a wicked man!' they said.

Then Zacchaeus turned to Jesus. 'Lord,' he said, 'I know that I am a dishonest cheat, but I want to change and put things right! I will give half of everything I own to the poor, and pay back everything I have stolen four times over.'

Jesus smiled at Zacchaeus and said, 'I have come to find and save anyone who has lost their way. Now change your heart and make a fresh start.'

Luke 19:1-10

Zaccheus
climbed a sycamore tree
to get a better view
of Jesus

How many names of trees can
you find in this wordsearch?

A	M	E	L	O	P	Y	E	T	R
E	U	C	A	L	Y	P	T	U	S
B	N	E	C	L	O	O	P	N	Y
A	R	D	E	W	W	P	S	T	R
O	U	A	R	I	F	L	E	S	R
L	B	R	O	L	S	A	R	E	E
P	A	R	S	L	M	R	A	H	H
C	L	L	A	O	E	R	O	C	C
B	A	D	A	W	E	Y	L	M	P
K	L	K	S	W	Y	W	A	S	H

You should
find twelve!

Day 22

The lost son

Jesus told this parable:

There was a man who had two sons and the younger one came to his father and said, 'Father, give me everything that will one day belong to me, so I can enjoy my riches now.'

The father did this, and the son set off to look for adventure. He travelled to a distant land and spent all his money enjoying himself.

There was a famine in that land, and the young man found himself penniless and hungry. 'If I stay here I will surely starve,' he thought, so he decided to return to his father and ask for his forgiveness.

The father saw his son coming and ran to welcome him. As he hugged him, the young man said, 'Father, I am so sorry. I no longer deserve to be called your son.'

But the father told his servants to prepare a feast and to bring the finest clothes, and they began to celebrate.

Luke 15:11-23

Use the code to find out what the father said to his son

```
A  B  D  E  F  H  I  L  N  O  S  T  U  V  W
1  2  3  4  5  6  78 9 10 11 12 13 14 15
```

'
___ ___   ___ ___ ___   ___ ___ ___ ___   ___ ___ ___
 6   4   15   1 11   3   4   1   3   2 13 12

___ ___ ___   ___ ___   ___ ___   ___ ___ ___ ___ ___ !
 9 10 15   6   4   7 11   1   8   7 14   4

___ ___   ___ ___ ___
 6   4   15   1 11

___ ___ ___ ___   ___ ___ ___
 8 10 11 12   2 13 12

___ ___ ___   ___ ___   ___ ___
 9 10 15   6   4   7 11

___ ___ ___ ___ ___
 5 10 13   9   3   Luke 15:24

Day 23

Lost and found

Jesus told these parables:

If a shepherd with a hundred sheep discovered that one of those sheep had strayed from the flock and got lost, would he not leave the ninety-nine and search for the last one until he found it? Then he would carry it home, rejoicing, and call all his friends to celebrate with him and share his delight. In the same way, I tell you, there will be more rejoicing in heaven over one sinner who repents than over ninety-nine good people who have nothing to be sorry for.

Or suppose a woman had ten drachmas, and found that one of her precious coins was missing. Surely she would take a lamp and sweep the house from top to bottom, searching everywhere until she found that coin. Then she would call her friends to share her happiness at finding what she had lost. In the same way, God's angels rejoice and celebrate over one person who is sorry for their sins.

Luke 15:4-10

How did the
shepherd and the woman
feel when they found what
had been lost?

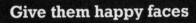
Give them happy faces

What does
God do when any
sinner returns to
his love?

Write the first letter
of each object

Day 24

Forgiveness

Peter came to Jesus and asked him, 'How many times must I forgive someone who does me wrong, Lord? Should it be as many as seven times?'

Jesus answered, 'Not just seven times, Peter, but as many as seventy-seven times!'

Then Jesus told a parable about the kingdom of heaven.

> There was once a king who had many servants. One servant owed the king a great deal of money, but he had nothing to pay him with. 'I will sell you and your family as slaves, and use the money to pay for your debts,' said the king.
>
> The servant fell to his knees and begged for another chance. 'Somehow I will repay everything I owe,' he pleaded. The king was a kind and generous man and, taking pity on the servant, cancelled his debts and let him go.
>
> Later that day, the same servant met another man who owed him a small amount of money. When he could not pay what he owed, the servant had him thrown into jail.
>
> When the news reached the king, he sent for the unforgiving servant. 'Could you not forgive someone just as I forgave you?' he asked. Then he had the servant thrown into prison until he could pay back all that he owed the king.

Jesus said, 'This is how my heavenly Father will treat you unless you forgive others with all your heart.'

Matthew 18:21-35

These two pictures might look the same but can you find six differences in the picture on the right?

Write the letter that is missing from the sequence in the box to spell out where the servant had the man sent

LMNOQ	
OPQST	
FGHJK	
PQRTU	
MNPQR	
KLMOP	

Matthew 18:30

Day 25

Prayer

When Jesus had finished praying, one of his disciples said to him, 'Master, teach us how to pray, just as John the Baptist taught his disciples.'

So Jesus said to them:

This is what to say when you pray:

Heavenly Father, holy is your name,
may your kingdom come;
each day give us our daily bread,
and forgive our sins,
as we forgive those who do us wrong,
and do not put us to the test.

Luke 11:1-4

Colour the picture using the number key given below

1	2	3	4	5	6
Blue	Brown	Pink	Yellow	Green	Orange

Mothering Sunday

Mothers

After the angel Gabriel had appeared to Mary, she set off at once to visit her cousin Elizabeth. When Elizabeth saw Mary coming, she ran to welcome her, and the baby inside her leapt for joy at the sound of Mary's words of greeting. Elizabeth was filled with the Holy Spirit and said to Mary, 'Of all women you are the most blessed, and blessed is the unborn child you are expecting, because you chose to believe in the power of God and the promise he made to you. I am honoured that the mother of my Lord should come to visit me.'

Luke 1:39-45

Can you find and circle the words in the puzzle below?

KIND   LOVING   GENEROUS   FORGIVING

PRECIOUS   GENTLE   THOUGHTFUL

S	A	H	G	E	O	L	N	L	T
M	G	E	N	E	R	O	U	S	H
E	E	F	I	Q	P	V	M	Y	O
F	N	I	V	K	Z	I	D	E	U
G	T	G	I	S	T	N	F	A	G
O	L	V	G	U	I	G	N	I	H
P	E	J	R	K	R	C	J	A	T
Q	S	U	O	I	C	E	R	P	F
S	B	W	F	G	Q	P	M	L	U
M	C	B	R	X	H	K	O	D	L

Day 27

The greatest commandment

The Pharisees asked Jesus a question which was meant to trick him. 'Which of the commandments is the greatest?' they asked.

Jesus answered, 'You must love the Lord your God with all your heart, and all your soul and with all your mind; this is the first and most important commandment.'

Matthew 22:34-38

Unscramble the words

Day 28

The Good Samaritan

A man asked Jesus a question: 'Who is my neighbour?'

Jesus told him this story:

> One day a man was travelling from Jerusalem to Jericho when a gang of robbers attacked him. They beat him up, and after stealing everything he had, they left him lying injured by the roadside. A short time later one of the Temple priests passed that way, but he crossed the road and walked on. Soon another traveller came, but he too passed by. Then a Samaritan happened to pass, and when he saw the injured man he took pity on him. He bandaged his wounds, and carried him on horseback to a nearby inn. There he cared for him and when the time came to leave, he left the innkeeper enough money to pay for the man's room until he was better.

Jesus then asked the man, 'Which man in the story was a good neighbour?'

'The one who helped the wounded traveller,' he answered.

'Go then and do the same for anyone who needs your help.'

Luke 10:30-37

Two men passed by and did not stop to help. Then a Samaritan took pity on the traveller and cared for him

Name four things which the Good Samaritan used to take care of the traveller

1. _____

2. _____

3. _____

4. _____

Circle the clues in the picture!

Day 29

Who am I?

One day Jesus asked his disciples, 'Who do people say that I am?'

'Some people say that you are John the Baptist; others say that you are Elijah or Jeremiah or one of the other wise prophets from the past.'

Then Jesus said, 'But who do you say that I am?'

The disciples were silent until Peter said, 'You are the Christ, the Son of the living God.'

Matthew 16:13-16

> **Jesus was delighted that Peter knew the answer!**

Use the code to find what Jesus said in Matthew 16:17

SECRET CODE PAD

5 = YOU   4 = REVEALED   3 = THIS

8 = HEAVENLY   9 = FATHER   14 = HAS

12 = MY   6 = TO

'

| _____ | _____ | _____ |
| 4 x 3 | 16 ÷ 2 | 6 + 3 |

| _____ | _____ | _____ |
| (3 + 4) x 2 | 11 − 7 | 9 ÷ 3 |

,

| _____ | _____ |
| 18 ÷ 3 | 8 − 3 |

Day 30

Jesus predicts his death

Jesus began to tell his disciples that he would be brought before the high priests in Jerusalem, and would be put to death before rising to life again.

Matthew 16:21

**Use the picture clues to complete the puzzle.
The letters in the bold boxes will spell out his name**

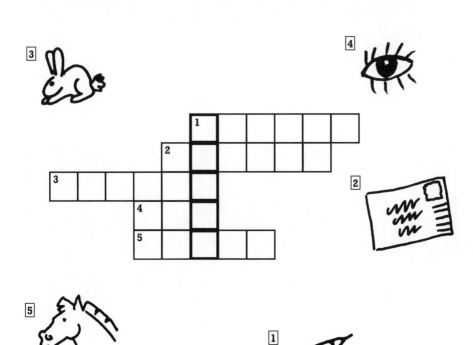

Day 31

It's hard to follow Jesus

Jesus told his disciples:

> If anyone wants to follow me, then they must take up their cross and put their own needs aside. Anyone who gives up their life for me will truly live. How can it be worth having the world if it means giving up life itself? Once life is lost, then it has gone for ever!

Matthew 16:24-25

Jesus told us what we must do if we are to follow him. Colour each square with a * and cross out each square with a •. Write the remaining letters in order on the lines below

START

*M	T	•O
A	•P	K

E	*K	*E	U	•S	P	•P
*L	Y	•J	O	*E	U	•R
R	•M	C	•B	R	*L	O

•J	S	S
A	*O	N
•K	D	F
O	*E	L
L	O	•J
*U	W	•O
M	*R	E

'TAKE

UP

YOUR

CROSS

AND

FOLLOW

ME'

Day 32

The rich man and Lazarus

One day Jesus told this story:

Once there was a rich man who had fine clothes and the best of everything that money could buy. He spent his time enjoying himself and feasting with his rich friends.

On the street outside his house lay a poor man called Lazarus who was thin and hungry, and covered in sores. Lazarus would gladly have eaten the rich man's scraps, if they had been offered to him. Lazarus died and went to heaven where Abraham took care of him, and he was truly happy at last.

When the rich man died he went to hell, and seeing Lazarus so happy, he cried out to Abraham for help.

Abraham said to him, 'You enjoyed a life of luxury and comfort, while Lazarus suffered. Now Lazarus is being consoled while it is your turn to suffer. It is too late to change things now.'

So the rich man begged Abraham to send someone from the dead to warn his brothers of what suffering awaited them unless they changed their ways.

Abraham said to him, 'They already know what to do! If they will not listen to Moses and the prophets, then even someone from the grave will not convince them!'

Luke 16:19-31

> The rich man enjoyed a good life while poor Lazarus suffered miserably

Use the words to fill in the blanks in this poem

CLOTHES   HEAVEN   RICH   EAT

WEALTH   LAZARUS   SORES   HEALTH

The _____ man lived in comfort and _____ .

He always looked a picture of _____ .

With elegant _____ and plenty to _____ ,

he did not see the man on the street.

_____ lay on the footpath outside,

hunger and sadness he could not hide.

Covered in _____ , with nobody's love,

his comfort would come in _____ above.

Fifth Sunday

The foolish man

Jesus told this parable:

Once there was a rich man who owned many farms. One year the harvest was so good that the man could not store it all in his many barns.

'I will build bigger and better barns,' he said, 'and then I will be so rich that I will have nothing to worry about.'

But God said to the man, 'You are a foolish man! When you die, what use will your worldly riches be, because in the eyes of God you are poor indeed.'

Luke 12:16-21

The rich man was foolish and greedy. He chose to store up his earthly riches instead of treasure in heaven

Circle these words in the puzzle below

**SELFISH   GREEDY   FOOLISH   RICH
TREASURE   BARNS   CROPS**

H	B	A	R	N	S	G	E
E	S	M	H	C	I	R	H
O	L	I	R	B	U	E	S
F	R	O	F	S	A	E	I
B	P	K	A	L	M	D	L
S	N	E	L	A	E	Y	O
P	R	L	A	E	M	S	O
T	A	R	E	S	A	M	F

Day 34

The rich man turns away

A man came to Jesus and asked, 'Good Master, what must I do if I want to have eternal life?'

Jesus asked him, 'Why do you call me good, when you know that only God is good?' Then he said to the man, 'You already know the commandments given by God. Do not commit murder; do not commit adultery; do not steal or falsely accuse anyone; do not cheat; and always respect your parents.'

'I have always tried to live according to these rules,' the man replied.

Jesus looked at the man kindly, and said, 'Then this is what you must do: sell everything you own, and give all your money away, for by doing this you will have riches in heaven. Then come and follow me.'

The man was sad because he was very wealthy.

Mark 10:17-22

Add or subtract letters to see what Jesus said in Mark 10:25

A B C D E F G H I J K L M N O P Q R S T U V W X Y Z

I __ __ __ E __ __ I R __ __ R
L+8 F+3 M+6 D−3 Q+2 B+3 K−5 N+1

__ C __ E __ __ __ P A __ __
G−6 J−9 I+4 V−10 O+5 S−4 W−4 B+17

__ __ R U H __ A
Z−6 G+1 P−1 D+3

__ __ E __ L E' __ __ __ , __ T H __ __
K+3 J−5 B+2 Q+2 L−7 X+1 A+4   I−8 M+1

__ __ R __ __ C H M A __
O−9 L+3 P−15 H+10 H+1 Q−3

__ __ T R __ __ __ __ E __ !
U−1 J+5 R−13 G+7 F−1 A+7 K−6 O−14 U+1 X−10

Day 35

God's or Caesar's?

The Pharisees wanted to trick Jesus into saying something which would get him into trouble. So they went to him and said, 'We know that you are honest and are not afraid to speak the truth. Tell us then, should we pay taxes to Caesar or not?'

Jesus answered, 'Why do you want to trick me? Show me your money.'

They gave him a Roman denarius and he asked them, 'Who is the person on this coin?'

'Caesar,' they answered.

Then Jesus said, 'Pay Caesar what belongs to him, and pay to God what belongs to God.'

When the Pharisees heard this they were amazed, and they went away.

Matthew 22:15-22

Here is a tricky question for you to answer!

Can you match each coin with the country where it is used?

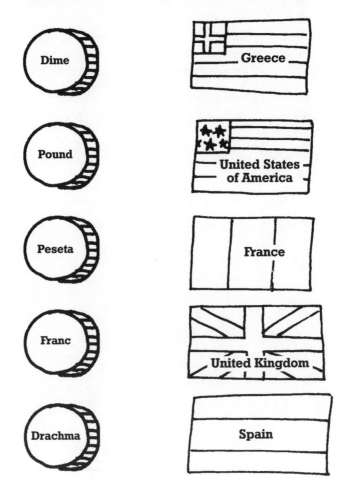

Day 36

Jesus is transfigured

One day Jesus asked Peter, James and John to come and pray with him. He led them to the top of a steep mountain, where it was peaceful and quiet, and where they could be alone.

Jesus began to pray to his heavenly Father and suddenly he appeared to change! His face and clothes shone with a brilliant light, as dazzling as the rays of the sun.

Then the disciples saw Moses and Elijah on either side of Jesus, talking to him. Peter jumped up with excitement and said, 'Lord, this is wonderful! I could make three shelters – one for each of you!'

At that moment a cloud streaming with light appeared above them, and a voice said, 'This is my Son, whom I love very much. Listen to what he says.'

The disciples were so terrified that they threw themselves to the ground and hid their faces.

Then Jesus said gently, 'Get up, my friends, do not be afraid.'

When they looked up, Jesus was standing alone.

Matthew 17:1-8

Jesus shone like the sun and his clothes became brilliant white – he was transfigured!

Use the clues to spell a word which explains what 'transfigured' means

1. The fourth letter of

2. The first letter of

3. The second letter of

4. The third letter of

5. The fourth letter of

6. The fourth letter of

7. The first letter of

Day 37

The three servants

Jesus told the people a parable.

The master of a household was going abroad for some time, so he called for his servants and said to them, 'I am splitting my property between you according to your skill for managing it.'

He gave each servant a number of talents. To the first he gave five talents, to the second he gave two and the third man received one. The first two men used their talents wisely, and soon doubled the amount they had been given. The man who received only one talent hid it away out of sight.

A long time later, the master of the house returned from his travels and called for his servants to see how they had invested his money. The first two servants stepped forward and presented him with double the amount they had been given.

'Well done,' the master said. 'Now I know that you can be trusted with small amounts I shall certainly trust you with more. Come and celebrate with me!'

Then the third servant stepped forward and returned to his master exactly what he had been given. His master was furious and said to him, 'You useless, lazy man! Even if you had simply put this amount in the bank, with interest it would have made more!'

He took the talent from his servant and gave it to the other who already had ten. 'To everyone who has something, even more will be given,' he said. 'Those who have little will have even that taken away.'

Then he had the lazy servant thrown out, while he celebrated with the other two.

Matthew 25:14-30

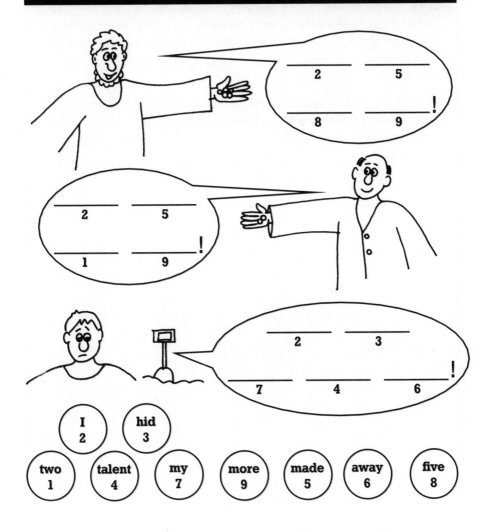

Day 38

Martha and Mary

One day Jesus and his disciples came to the village called Bethany where his friends Martha and Mary lived. They welcomed Jesus and his followers and invited them to stay for a meal.

While Martha busied herself preparing and serving the food, her sister Mary sat calmly beside Jesus and listened to him talking. Martha worked hard, and all the while Mary sat listening to Jesus. Finally Martha got upset and said to Jesus, 'Lord, must I do all this work on my own? Tell Mary to come and help me!'

'Martha, Martha,' Jesus said, 'do not let these things upset you, they are not important. Mary has chosen to listen to me and that is the most important thing of all.'

Luke 10:38-42

Martha busied herself serving her guests, while Mary sat next to Jesus and listened to him speaking

Martha felt angry with her sister! What did she say?

Use the code to read her words

Day 39

The two builders

Jesus said:

Whoever listens to me and obeys my words is like a wise man who built his house on rock. The wind howled, the rain poured down and the rivers burst their banks and flooded the land. The house built on rock stood firm and did not fall. But whoever listens to me and disobeys my words is like a foolish man who built his house on sand. The wind howled, and the rain poured down and the rivers burst their banks and flooded the land. The house collapsed and fell because it was built on sand.

Matthew 7:24-27

What did the sensible man do?

Write the first letter of each picture clue to spell out the answer

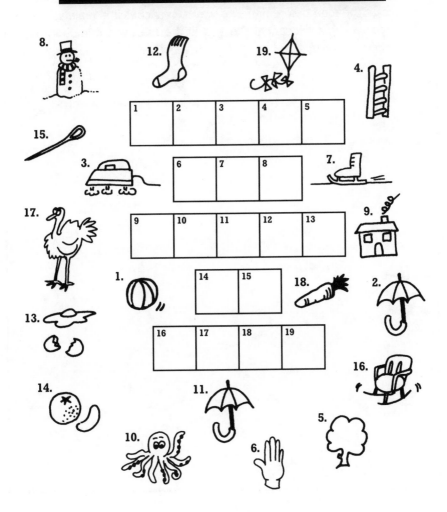

Palm Sunday

Riding into Jerusalem

The two disciples brought a young colt, and after throwing a cloak on its back, Jesus climbed on, and continued on his journey to Jerusalem.

Many people had lined the road to greet Jesus, and they spread their cloaks on the road before him, and waved branches in the air, as they shouted with joy, 'Hosanna! Blessed is the one who comes in the name of the Lord.'

Mark 11:7-10

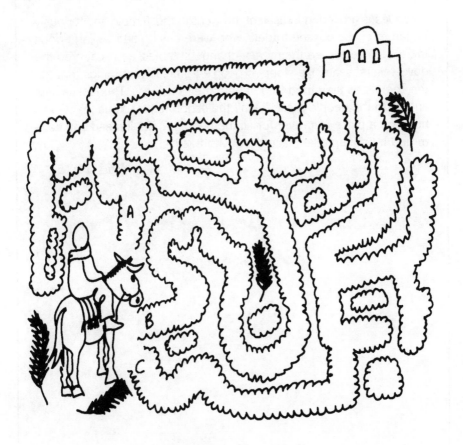

Monday of Holy Week

Jesus in the Temple

When Jesus arrived in Jerusalem, he went to the Temple and furiously began to chase out the traders who were buying and selling goods there. He overturned the money-changers' tables, and scattered the dove-sellers' seats. He stopped people from carrying things through the Temple as they tried to go about their business. Then Jesus said angrily to the people there, 'Don't the scriptures teach us that God's house is a place of prayer for all the peoples? But instead you have turned it into a marketplace filled with thieves!'

Mark 11:15-17

He drove the animals and traders out of the Temple

How many differences can you find in the bottom picture? Circle the number

6   8   10   12

Tuesday of Holy Week

Jesus is anointed

Six days before the Passover, Jesus arrived in Bethany, the home town of Lazarus, the friend he had raised from the dead. Lazarus and his sisters, Martha and Mary, gave a dinner for Jesus. While they were at table, Mary brought in some pure nard oil, a very expensive perfume. She knelt and anointed the feet of Jesus with the nard, wiping it away with her hair, until the room was filled with its fragrance.

Seeing this, Judas Iscariot, the disciple who would soon betray Jesus, asked, 'Why did she not sell this perfume and give the money to the poor?' Judas was in charge of the common purse, and was not so much worried about the needs of the poor, but about helping himself to the money.

Jesus said to Judas, 'Leave Mary alone. Let her keep this perfume and use it for my burial, for you will always have the poor with you, but you will not always have me.'

John 12:1-8

Use the code to find out what Mary did for Jesus

♥	S	H	A	N	I
♦	R	U	E	D	W
✾	F	T	P	M	O
	A	B	C	D	E

♥A ♥B ♦C

♥C ♥D ✾E ♥E ♥D ✾B ♦C ♦D

♥B ♥E ♥A   ✾A ♦C ♦C ✾B   ♦E ♥E ✾B ♥B

✾C ♦B ♦A ♦C   ♥D ♥C ♦A ♦D

♥C ♥D ♦D   ♦E ♥E ✾C ♦C ♦D   ✾B ♥B ♦C ✾D

♦E ♥E ✾B ♥B   ♥B ♦C ♦A

♥B ♥C ♥E ♦A

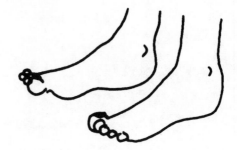

Wednesday of Holy Week

The vineyard

Jesus told another parable to the people.

There was once a farmer who owned a vineyard. He had to go away on business, and so he put some farm workers in charge of the vineyard. When it was time to harvest the grapes, the farmer sent some servants to collect his share. But the farm workers beat his servants and chased them away. The farmer did not give up, and sent more servants to collect what belonged to him. Again, they were beaten and chased off.

Finally the farmer sent his own son. 'I am sure that they will treat him better,' he said.

Instead the farm workers seized the son and killed him.

Matthew 21:33-39

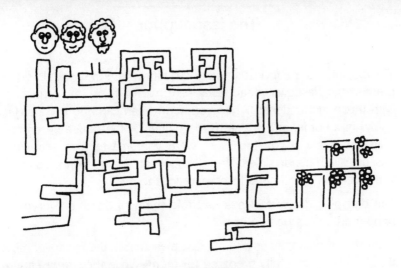

Use the code cracker to find out what the farmers are plotting!

A 1	N 14
B 2	O 15
C 3	P 16
D 4	Q 17
E 5	R 18
F 6	S 19
G 7	T 20
H 8	U 21
I 9	V 22
J 10	W 23
K 11	X 24
L 12	Y 25
M 13	Z 26

'
12 5 20 19

11 9 12 12

8 9 13   1 14 4

20 1 11 5   8 9 19

9 14 8 5 18 9 20 1 14 3 5 !'

Maundy Thursday

The last supper

The disciples came to Jesus and asked him where they should go to prepare the Passover meal. Jesus sent two of them into Jerusalem with these instructions: 'When you see a man carrying a water jar, follow him home, and speak to the owner of the house he enters. Ask him to show you the room were your master can share the Passover with his disciples. He will show you a large furnished room with everything you need to prepare for the meal.'

The disciples did what Jesus had told them to do, and everything happened just as he had said.

Later that evening, Jesus and his disciples shared the Passover meal that had been carefully prepared for them. While they were eating, Jesus told his friends, 'I am about to be betrayed by one of you sharing this very meal with me.'

The disciples were upset by these words, and one after another they asked Jesus, 'Lord, you do not mean me, do you?'

Jesus replied, 'It will be one of you who even now dips his bread into the same bowl as I do. It would be better for my betrayer that he had never been born.'

As they were eating, Jesus took some bread which he blessed and broke. Then he shared it with them saying these words, 'Take this, for it is my body.'

Next he blessed a cup of wine, and again he shared it with the disciples, saying to them, 'This is my blood, poured out for many, which seals God's new covenant. I will not drink this wine again, until I drink the new wine in God's kingdom.'

When they had sung a psalm together, Jesus and his disciples made their way to the Mount of Olives on the outskirts of the city.

Mark 14:12-26

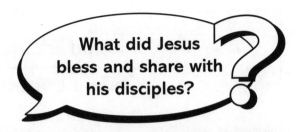

What did Jesus bless and share with his disciples?

Fit the numbered words in place to reveal the answer!

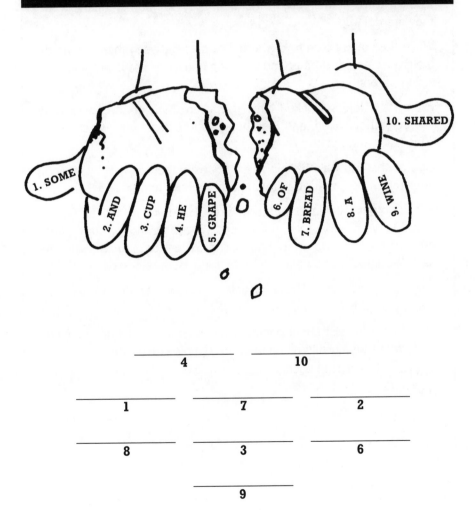

———— ————
4   10

———— ———— ————
1   7   2

———— ———— ————
8   3   6

————
9

Good Friday

Jesus is crucified

Two others were led out to be put to death with Jesus, and when they reached the place called the skull, they were crucified, one on his right and the other on his left.

Jesus prayed, 'Father, forgive them, for they do not understand what they are doing.'

While they threw dice to divide his clothes between them, some of the crowd jeered: 'If he is God's chosen one let him save himself; he's saved others!'

Even the soldiers mocked him, 'If you are King of the Jews, save yourself,' they called, and they hung a sign above him which read, 'This is the King of the Jews.'

One of the criminals hanging next to Jesus taunted him by saying, 'Aren't you the Christ? Can't you save yourself and us as well?'

But the other criminal scolded the first. 'Have you no fear of God?' he said. 'We deserve this punishment! We are paying for our crimes, but this man has done nothing wrong.' Then, turning to Jesus, he said, 'Jesus, when you come into your kingdom remember me.'

Jesus answered him, 'This very day I promise that you will be with me in paradise.'

Then about the sixth hour darkness fell upon the land, until the ninth hour, when the curtain hanging in the temple was torn in two.

In a loud voice Jesus cried out, 'Father, I place my spirit in your hands!' And then he died.

Luke 24:32-46

The soldiers fixed a notice to the cross above Jesus.

Write the first letter of each picture clue to read what it said

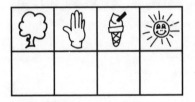

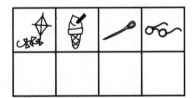

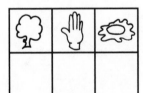

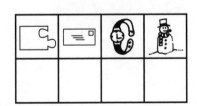

Holy Saturday

The burial of Jesus

After the death of Jesus, one of his followers, a man called Joseph who came from the town of Arimathea, went to Pontius Pilate and asked if he could take the body down from the cross to be buried. Pilate agreed, and with the help of another disciple called Nicodemus, Joseph wrapped Jesus' body in linen cloths and spices, according to the Jewish custom at that time. In a garden, close to the place where Jesus had been crucified, was a fresh tomb which had never been used. Since it was already late on the day before the Sabbath celebration, they took Jesus to this tomb nearby and laid him to rest there.

John 19:38-42

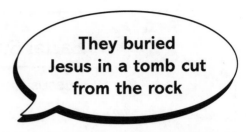

They buried Jesus in a tomb cut from the rock

Use the code to find another name for a tomb

	1	2	3	4
✖	C	P	A	H
❋	S	K	J	E
▲	E	R	U	L

__
3✖

___ ___ ___ ___ ___ ___ ___ ___ ___
1❋ 1▲ 2✖ 3▲ 4▲ 1✖ 4✖ 2▲ 4❋

Easter Sunday

Jesus is alive!

At sunrise on the Sunday morning some of the women took the burial spices they had prepared and went to the tomb where Jesus had been laid.

To their surprise they found that the stone had been rolled away from the entrance to the tomb, and the body of Jesus was gone.

As they stood wondering what had happened, two angels appeared next to them and asked, 'Why do you look for the living among the dead? Remember how he told you that he would rise again on the third day. He is not here because he is risen!

Luke 24:1-7

Write the word that fits the clue. The first letter of each answer will spell out a word which means 'rising from the dead'

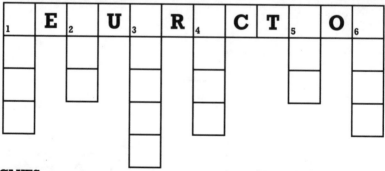

| 1 | E | 2 | U | 3 | R | 4 | C | T | 5 | O | 6 |

CLUES

1. Water falling from clouds
2. Bright object in the sky
3. Red-breasted bird
4. Birds lay these
5. Frozen water
6. You use this to smell with